CHAPTER ONE:
MULHOLLAND DRIVE

HOLLYWOOD HILLS. AFTERNOON.

WHAT THE...?

X-MEN ORIGINS:

DEADPOOL

"THE MAJOR MOTION PICTURE"

Duane Swierczynski **Leandro Fernandez** **Steve Buccellato** **Jeff Eckleberry** **Taylor Esposito**
Writer Art Colors Letters Production

Sebastian Girner **Axel Alonso** **Joe Quesada** **Dan Buckley** **Alan Fine**
Asst. Editor Editor Editor in Chief Publisher Exec. Producer

YOUR AGENT TOLD YOU *THE DEAL*, RIGHT?

EVERY-THING'S TURNED INTO A MOVIE THESE DAYS -- OLD TV SHOWS, BOARD GAMES, CANDY BARS. AND LEMME TELL YA, I'M TOTALLY STOKED FOR *BUTTERFINGER: THE MOVIE.*

ANYWAY, I FIGURE SOONER OR LATER, THEY'RE GOING TO GET AROUND TO ME. BUT I WANT TO BEAT HOLLYWOOD TO THE *PUNCH*.

I'VE BEEN INTERVIEWING SCREENWRITERS ALL DAY. THE LAST TWO...

WELL, THOSE DIDN'T GO SO WELL.

THIRTY-EIGHT MINUTES AGO.

LISTEN, DAWG -- WE GO ALL MICHAEL BAY ON THIS MOTHER. I'M TALKING MONSTER BRAWLS, HUGE ACTION SET PIECES. YOU VS. SASQUATCH. YOU VS. HULK. YOU VS. ...

WAIT, CAN WE GET THE RIGHTS TO THE HULK? I DON'T KNOW, DOESN'T MATTER...

UH, YEAH, I WAS KIND OF THINKING...

DON'T BE LIKE THAT, BRO. DON'T BE STUCK IN THE OLD PARADIGM. YOU'VE GOT TO GO *HIGH-CONCEPT!*

THIS HIGH? OR MAYBE A LITTLE *HIGHER*?

WAIT. WHAT ARE YOU...

SO... WHAT'VE *YOU* GOT?

I DON'T *"HAVE"* ANY-THING.

I'M HERE TO LISTEN. I JUST WANT TO HEAR YOUR STORY.

YOU MEAN YOU DON'T WANT TO GIVE ME YOUR PITCH? TELL ME *YOUR VERSION OF MY LIFE?*

NOPE.

OKAY, THEN BUDDY. HERE'S MY STORY. YOU MIGHT BE SORRY YOU ASKED.

AFTER ALL, IT IS AN *ORIGIN* STORY...

"...AND LIKE SO MANY ORIGIN STORIES, IT STARTS OFF WITH ME *BUTT NEKKID* AND IN A *CRAZY-RIDICULOUS* AMOUNT OF PAIN."

CHAPTER TWO:
THE NAKED
AND THE DEAD

"YOU MAY ASK: HOW DID I END UP IN THIS TANK FULL OF WATER, SHARP NEEDLES JABBIN' MY YIN-YANG AND TUBES UP MY HOO-HAH-AND-HOW'S-YER-MOTHER?"

"I, UH... *VOLUNTEERED*."

"SEE, IT WAS EITHER PAINFUL DEATH FROM *STAGE IV CANCER* -- OR THESE *EXPERIMENTAL TRIALS* UP IN CANADA.

"(I KNOW. THE CANADA THING GAVE ME PAUSE, TOO.)

"AND LOOKING BACK ON WHAT HAPPENED, SOME MIGHT SAY I SHOULD HAVE TAKEN MY CHANCES WITH THE BIG C."

OH GOD.

WHAT *IN THE NAME OF...*

WHAT? IS IT MY *HAIR?*

CRAP, DID I LOSE SOME OF MY HAIR?

"AS THE DOCS EXPLAINED IT, THE EXPERIMENT WAS A *MIXED BAG.*

"SURE MY BODY COULD REGENERATE ITSELF AT AMAZING SPEEDS."

BLAM

HEY! DON'T YOU WANT TO START WITH A *TOE,* OR SOMETHING --

ACK... IS IT... SUPPOSED TO... HURT... SO MUCH...

WHOA.

HE'S STILL UGLY.

HANG ON. I THINK I CAN FIX THIS.

AHH!

GUSHHHHH

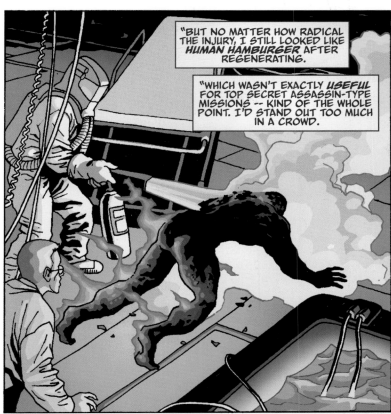

"BUT NO MATTER HOW RADICAL THE INJURY, I STILL LOOKED LIKE *HUMAN HAMBURGER* AFTER REGENERATING.

"WHICH WASN'T EXACTLY *USEFUL* FOR TOP SECRET ASSASSIN-TYPE MISSIONS -- KIND OF THE WHOLE POINT. I'D STAND OUT TOO MUCH IN A CROWD.

"THEY TOLD ME NOT TO WORRY. WHILE THEY SORTED IT OUT, I COULD CHILL OUT AT A *RESORT* TO RECOVER.

"AND IT WAS A REAL *CLUB MED*.

"IF BY CLUB MED YOU MEAN *CLUB* FAILED *MED*-ICAL EXPERIMENTS.

"ROTTING AWAY IN MY CELL, I REALIZED I SIGNED ON FOR A FATE WORSE THAN CANCER. AT LEAST CANCER ENDS. THIS WENT ON AND ON...POTENTIALLY *FOREVER*.

"I HAD TO FIND A WAY OUT."

"AFTER MY ESCAPE, I FELL BACK ON THE WHOLE MERCENARY THING. ONLY NOW, I HAD CERTAIN *COMPETITIVE ADVANTAGES* OVER MY... UH... COMPETITION.

"(YOU'RE THE WRITER -- YOU'LL MASSAGE THIS CRAP, RIGHT?)

"I ALSO DECIDED TO WEAR A MASK, JUST LIKE THE PEOPLE IN THE FUNNYBOOKS.

"BUT ALONG WITH THE MASK AND SUPER-POWERS CAME SOME *TRULY WEIRD* GIGS.

"LIKE ONE OF MY EARLIEST ASSIGNMENTS -- KILLING THIS *GRUMPY CYBORG MUTANT* FROM THE FUTURE.

WHEN I FROST YOUR SORRY OLD MECHANICAL BUTT, DON'T TAKE IT PERSONALLY, OKAY?

NO PROBLEM.

"PREDICTABLY, WE ENDED UP *BEST FRIENDS.*

"SO ANYWAY..."

"WAIT WAIT. YOU'RE SKIPPING THE MOST IMPORTANT PART."

WHAT'S THAT?

TELL ME MORE ABOUT *WADE WILSON.* THE MAN, BEFORE HE PUT ON THE MASK. BEFORE THE WEAPON X EXPERIMENT. BEFORE EVERY-THING.

HUH. YOU WANT TO HEAR THE TRUTH ABOUT *WADE WILSON?*

"HE WAS AN *IDIOT.*"

CHAPTER THREE:
INGLORIOUS BASTERD

"WADE WILSON WAS A MERCENARY WITH A MORAL CODE -- ONLY TOOK JOBS HE "BELIEVED" IN. HE WAS MORE EARNEST THAN A LIFETIME ORIGINAL MOVIE.

"IN FACT, WADE WILSON WAS PRETTY MUCH THE ONLY MERCENARY ALIVE WHO WASN'T IN IT FOR THE MONEY.*

*MERCENARY (mur-suh-ner-ee): Some dude who's in it for the money.

"HE'D GO OUT, KILL SOME DIRTBAG DICTATOR WHO 'DESERVED' IT...

"...THEN GO HOME TO HIS HOTTIE GIRLFRIEND IN BOSTON."

WADE! OH, THE THINGS I'M GOING TO DO TO YOUR BODY... AFTER YOU SHOWER, OF COURSE...

"WHAT CAN I SAY? HE WAS YOUNG. LIFE HADN'T THROWN HIM ANY SURPRISES. YET."

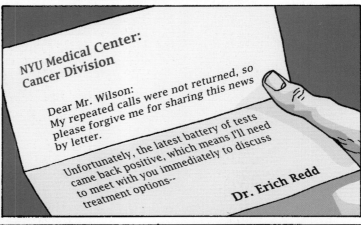

NYU Medical Center:
Cancer Division

Dear Mr. Wilson:
My repeated calls were not returned, so please forgive me for sharing this news by letter.

Unfortunately, the latest battery of tests came back positive, which means I'll need to meet with you immediately to discuss treatment options--

Dr. Erich Redd

"BUT I... ER, I MEAN, *WADE WILSON* REFUSED.

"LONG AGO, HE SWORE NOT TO BE A BURDEN TO ANYBODY -- ESPECIALLY NOT THOSE HE LOVED. SO HE HIT THE ROAD.

"AND SOMETIMES, THE ROAD HIT BACK.

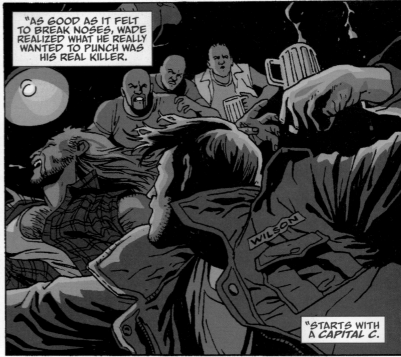

"AS GOOD AS IT FELT TO BREAK NOSES, WADE REALIZED WHAT HE REALLY WANTED TO PUNCH WAS HIS REAL KILLER.

"STARTS WITH A *CAPITAL C.*

"JUST WHEN IT SEEMED HOPELESS, HE RAN INTO ANOTHER MERC-FOR-HIRE WHO TOLD HIM ABOUT THIS *CRAZY MEDICAL EXPERIMENT UP IN CANADA...*"

ANNNND YOU KNOW WHAT HAPPENS FROM THERE. NEEDLES UP THE YIN-YANG, ET CETERA ET CETERA.

MOVING ON TO THE COOL STUFF...

NO, NO. THIS IS GREAT. LET'S PROBE DEEPER.

TELL ME MORE ABOUT THE YOUNG WADE WILSON. BEFORE HE WAS A MERC FOR HIRE. *BEFORE* HE WAS AN ADULT, EVEN. WHAT WAS HIS CHILD-HOOD LIKE?

WHAT, IS THIS -- *DIARY OF A WIMPY MERC?* NOBODY WANTS TO HEAR THAT STUFF.

I'M NOT JOKING! THIS IS THE *EMOTIONAL CENTER** OF THE WHOLE MOVIE! CAN'T SEE THAT?

*EMOTIONAL CENTER (e-mo-shun-ul cen-tur): A word screenwriters use to impress chicks.

JOKING, HUH?

MY DAD WAS A REAL KIDDER.

"WE HAD A ROUTINE: HE'D SLIP BEHIND OUR FRONT DOOR, AND THEN..."

NOK NOK

WHO'S THERE?

CASH.

CASH WHO?

CASHEW? I ALWAYS *KNEW* YOU WERE A NUT!

AWWW DAD, THAT'S YOUR WORST ONE YET!

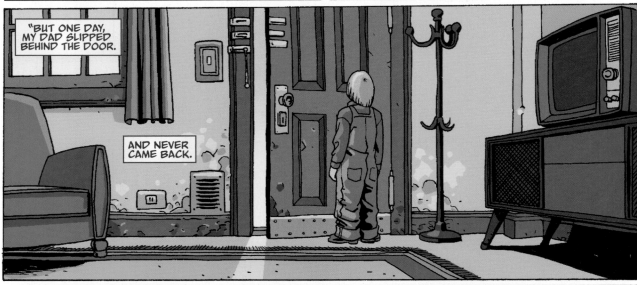

"BUT ONE DAY, MY DAD SLIPPED BEHIND THE DOOR.

AND NEVER CAME BACK.

"I'D DO OUR KNOCK-KNOCK ROUTINE, JUST TO SEE IF HE WAS *WAITING ME OUT.*"

NOK NOK

WHO'S THERE?

"HE WASN'T."

CHAPTER FOUR:
A STAR IS BORN

"AFTER MY DAD LEFT, MY MOM TRIED TO EASE THE PAIN WITH BOOZE AND ORDERING JUNK FROM CABLE TV CHANNELS."

GO ON HONEY, FIX YERRRSELF SOMETHING. MOMMY'S HAVING *FRUIT SALAD.*

"SHE JOKED ABOUT EVERYTHING -- EVEN THE CRIPPLING DEBT SHE'D RACKED UP."

WHEN LIFE HANDS YOU LEMMENS... MAKE ANOTHER GIN AND TONNNIC!

"I BLAMED MYSELF. SHE'D BE FINE, IF SHE DIDN'T HAVE ME TO WORRY ABOUT.

"I SWORE I WOULDN'T BE A BURDEN TO ANY-BODY, EVER AGAIN."

WADE? *WAAAAAYYYYYDE* HONEY?

"WHEN I WAS OLD ENOUGH, I TOOK ADVANTAGE OF THE *ONE OPPORTUNITY* OPEN TO BROKE YOUNG AMERICANS EVERYWHERE."

"MY SUPERIORS SAID I WAS A *CRACK SHOT* WITH A *GREAT TACTICAL MIND*. A BORN *SURVIVOR*."

"I DIDN'T HAVE THE HEART TO TELL THEM THAT'S BECAUSE I PRACTICALLY GREW UP WITH A JOYSTICK IN MY HAND."

"NO, I DON'T MEAN *THAT* KIND OF -- OH, NEVER MIND."

"AFTER MY ARMY STINT, I GOT INTO BUSINESS FOR MYSELF. AS LONG AS I AGREED WITH THE CAUSE, I'D PULL THE TRIGGER."

"GOT A DICTATOR DOIN' SOME ETHNIC CLEANSING? I'D *RUB HIM OUT* FOR YA."

"SOME "ELECTED" OFFICIAL STARVING HIS PEOPLE? I'D MAKE HIM *CHOKE ON HIS OWN BLOOD*."

"*NOW* ISN'T ALL THAT DIFFERENT FROM *THEN*, COME TO THINK OF IT."

"*EXCEPT* I DON'T GIVE A CRAP ABOUT *THE CAUSE*."

YOU CARE TOO MUCH, YOU BLEED.

"SEE, I THINK MOM *HAD IT RIGHT* ALL ALONG.

"WHEN YOU'RE CONFRONTED WITH *A HORRIBLE SITUATION*, THERE ARE ONLY TWO REACTIONS THAT MAKE SENSE: LAUGHTER OR TEARS.

HUH -- GUESS I'LL BE LETTING MY F-FINGERS DO THE WALKING...

"AND LAUGHTER, AFTER ALL, IS NATURE'S ANESTHESIA.

"TEARS HURT TOO MUCH."

SKUTCH

BOY, THE AIR CONDITIONING IS *CRAP* IN HERE.

YOU WOULDN'T BELIEVE HOW STUFFY IT IS UNDER ONE OF THESE THINGS.

ANYHOO...

THERE WAS THIS ONE TIME, I'M SQUARING OFF AGAINST THE HULK AND I'M ALL LIKE, "YO, JOLLY GREEN MOUTH BREATHER..."

I THINK WE HAVE ENOUGH.

WE... WE *DO?*

YOU'VE GIVEN ME PURE GOLD. THIS IS GOING TO BE AN *AMAZING* MOVIE.

THIRTY-FIVE MONTHS LATER.

WORLD PREMIERE TONIGHT

DEADPOOL: ORIGINS

IN IMAX 3D HD3 PLUS (ENHANCED)

HEY! *WADE!* SO GLAD YOU COULD MAKE IT.

STILL CAN'T BELIEVE THIS IS ALL REAL. I TRIED TO IGNORE THE REPORTS ON THE WEB AND GOSSIP MAGS -- I DIDN'T WANT TO GET MY HOPES UP.

YOU LIKED THE SCRIPT, RIGHT?

NO, THE SCRIPT WAS GREAT, IT'S JUST...

DON'T WORRY. IT'S *EVERYTHING* WE TALKED ABOUT.

YOU'RE GOING TO *LOVE* THIS.

CHAPTER FIVE:
KISS KISS BANG BANG

ONLY THEN DO I REALIZE THAT I DON'T NEED HOLLYWOOD.

I'VE BEEN LIVING IN MOVIES ALL MY LIFE.

IMAGINARY SCENARIOS, INSIDE MY BRAIN, MEANT TO DISTRACT ME FROM *THE PAIN OF REALITY.*

IMAGINARY SCENARIOS...

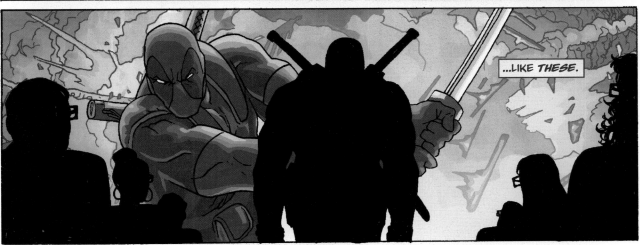

CHAPTER SIX:
THE LONG GOODBYE

I DUG UP THE ADDRESS YEARS AGO.

NEVER THOUGHT ABOUT USING IT UNTIL NOW.

RECLUSA PARDA, MEXICO.

NO OFFENSE, CARLOS, BUT WHEN YOU INVITED ME TO MEXICO, I EXPECTED SOMETHING A LITTLE MORE *MARGARITA-VILLE*...

...AND A LITTLE LESS *LA CUCARACHA*.

THIS ISN'T A VACATION, WADE! I ASKED YOU TO COME BECAUSE I DIDN'T KNOW WHO ELSE TO TURN TO FOR HELP!

MY PRIDE AND JOY -- MY BELLA -- HAS BEEN *KID-NAPPED*!

IT'S OKAY, PAL. I NEVER LET YOU DOWN WHEN WE WERE STUCK IN THAT HELLHOLE WITH BULLETS WHIZZING ALL AROUND OUR HEADS, DID I?

I'M NOT GONNA LET YOU DOWN NOW.

Hellhole? Bullets? You were in a T-ball league together!

BELLA WAS BACK HERE WHEN I SAW HER LAST...

LEMME JUST PUT ON MY CSI HAT AND TAKE A --

UH, CARLOS? WHEN YOU SAY KIDNAPPED... YOU *REALLY* MEAN "*KID*"-NAPPED, DON'T YOU?

MOUTH
OF THE BORDER
Cullen Bunn: Writer • Matteo Scalera: Art
Matt Wilson: Colors

I'M GUESSING THERE'S A REASON YOU SHOT THAT POOR WOMAN IN THE FACE?

DUH! PAPER OR PLASTIC? HELLOOO? YOU HAVE ANY IDEA WHAT PLASTIC BAGS DO TO THE ENVIRONMENT? I'M AL GORE'S MESSENGER OF DEATH, BEE-YOTCH!

WHILE WE'RE ON THE SUBJECT... YOU'VE TYPICALLY HAD TROUBLE WITH WOMEN IN THE PAST, HAVEN'T YOU, WADE?

"GEE, LET'S SEE...

"COPYCAT WAS TURNED INTO FISHFOOD BY SABRETOOTH.

"TYPHOID MARY MADE *ME* LOOK SANE.

"SIRYN WANTS NOTHING TO DO WITH ME.

"BLACK WIDOW HAD MY HEAD CUT OFF."

WHATEVER GAVE YOU THAT IDEA?

SO ANYWAY...

"IT WAS AROUND THIS TIME I TOOK A MEAT CLEAVER TO THE BACK OF THE HEAD."

NOW, WE'VE DISCUSSED THIS BEFORE. AS I RECALL, YOU HAVE THE ABILITY TO TAKE PHYSICAL PUNISHMENT DUE TO WHAT THE GOVERNMENT DID TO YOU.

THE WEAPON X PROGRAM, IF WE'RE GETTING TECHNICAL ABOUT IT.

"SURE, THEY CURED ME OF MY CANCER. SURE, THEY GAVE ME THIS KICK-ASS HEALING FACTOR.

"BUT THEY ALSO TURNED MY BODY INTO SIX FEET OF DOWNTOWN NEWARK."

YOUR FACE... IT BOTHERS YOU. DRIVES YOU TO DO THE THINGS YOU DO, DOESN'T IT?

I DON'T WANT TO TALK ABOUT IT.

BUT THAT'S WHAT WE'RE HERE FOR, WADE, TO--

I'M A BARBIE GIRL! IN A BARBIE WORLD! LIFE IN PLASTIC---IT'S FANTASTIC!

I'M NOT LISTENING!

"LOOK, THE WEAPON X PROGRAM...THEY TURNED ME INTO A KILLING MACHINE."

"SO THAT'S WHAT I DO.

"I KILL."

OKAY, FAIR ENOUGH. CONTINUE WITH YOUR STORY. I'M SURE THERE'S A POINT TO IT EVENTUALLY.

RIGHT, MOVING RIGHT ALONG...

"AT THIS POINT THE WHOLE JOINT TURNED ON ME.

"THE BAG BOY WITH THE LAZY EYE. THE MANAGER WITH DISTURBING MAN BOOBS. THE GEEKY CASHIER WITH PIMPLES THE SIZE OF GOLF BALLS. THE OLD LADY...

"THE OLD LADY.

"I HESITATED ON THE OLD LADY."

"WHY?"

"SHE...REMINDED ME OF SOMEONE."

IT'S YOUR FRIEND, BLIND AL, ISN'T IT?

YEAH.

TELL ME ABOUT HER. ABOUT YOUR... FRIENDS.

"WHAT'S TO TELL? I EITHER DRIVE 'EM ALL AWAY...

"OR WE END UP TRYING TO KILL EACH OTHER."

AND THE OLD WOMAN...WHAT HAPPENED TO HER, WADE?

WHAT DO YA THINK HAPPENED, DOC?

"THIS WAS ONE GOLDEN GIRL THAT WASN'T MAKIN' HER NEXT MAHJONG TOURNAMENT."

"I SEE. I THINK IT'S TIME TO GET TO THE POINT OF THIS STORY NOW, WADE."

"CUT TO THE CHASE IT IS THEN...

"IT WAS ALL A JOB. THE SUPERMARKET... THESE PEOPLE...ALL SECRETLY PART OF A TERRORIST ORGANIZATION CALLED G.O.A.L.

"GLOBAL OBLITERATION AND ANNIHILATION OF THE LOLLIPOP GUILD. OR SOMETHING LIKE THAT. WHAT DIFFERENCE DOES IT MAKE?"

"PEOPLE WANTED 'EM DEAD. AND I DEADED 'EM."

SO SAY HELLO TO THE BAD GUY!

IS THAT WHAT I'M SUPPOSED TO GET OUT OF THIS STORY, WADE? BECAUSE THAT'S NOT WHAT I'M GETTING OUT OF THIS.

OH NO, WHAT ARE YOU GETTING? GAS? IS IT GAS?

"BAD GUYS DON'T FIGHT THE THREATS YOU HAVE, WADE. BAD GUYS DON'T SAVE THE WORLD AS OFTEN AS YOU HAVE."

YOU CAN SPIN THIS HOWEVER YOU WANT, BUT WHAT I SEE IS A MAN WHO TOOK OUT A BURGEONING TERRORIST ORGANIZATION BEFORE THEY BECAME THE NEXT A.I.M. OR HYDRA.

I SEE A MAN WHO...

CAN SPARE A QUARTER?

WHAT?

IT'S EIGHTY BELOW AT THE NORTH POLE TONIGHT.

AND THIS JOINT'S LOCKED DOWN TIGHTER THAN THE PRESIDENT'S MISTRESS'S LOVE NEST.

SQUEE SQUEE SQUEE

BUT THAT'S WHY I GET THE BIG BUCKS.

BEE BEE BEE!

BANG!

CREATIVITY.

STAMPEDE!

ROUND 'EM UP QUICKLY! THEY'RE MORE RAPID THAN EAGLES!

AND IF YOU SEE WHO SPOOKED 'EM -- TAKE THE GRINCH OUT!